Printed and Published by D. C. Thomson & Co., Ltd.,
Dundee and London.

Twinkle

1998

Hi, everyone!

It's Twinkle Book time again! I hope you enjoy this super book that's packed with fun specially for you.

Old King Cold, Witchy Woo and The jungle pool are just some of the great stories inside.

There are lots of puzzles to do and exciting games to play.

Plus Nurse Nancy, Silly Milly, Patch, Sally and Scamp and all your favourite Twinkle chums in 64 colourful pages.

Have fun!

Love,

Twinkle.

Nurse Nancy

Nancy is the nurse at the Dollies Hospital where her grandad is the doctor. Colin is the ambulance boy.

1 — Leah Harris took her broken toy theatre to the Dollies Hospital one day. "Can you mend my theatre and Snow White doll?" she asked Nurse Nancy.

2 — Nancy examined the theatre dolls. "I had a show planned for today," said Leah, "but I'll have to cancel it. I've lost some dwarf dolls too," she sighed.

3 — "Don't worry," smiled Nancy. "While Grandad looks at your theatre, I'll see if any of the tiny dolls in the dolls' house can replace the dwarfs."

4 — Luckily, Grandad said the theatre could be mended quickly and Nancy did as she'd said. Colin took some patients out for a stroll to let Nancy help Leah.

5 — Soon afterwards, the dolls and theatre looked like new. "If I hurry, I can still put on today's show," Leah said, as she went off. She was delighted. "Thanks *ever* so much, Nancy!"

6 — Nancy's patients had hoped to see Leah's show, though. The little nurse knew they were disappointed, so she found her Twinkles.

7 — Nancy told Colin her plan and, together, they cut out pictures of Twinkle people. Then they stuck them to card and taped a drinking straw to each figure.

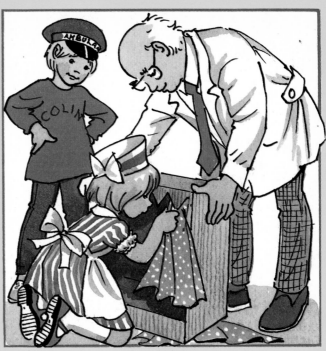

8 — Next, Grandad helped make a theatre from a box. Nancy stuck pretty curtains to the front while Grandad pinned a blue curtain to either end of the open back.

9 — Nancy and Colin practised at sliding the Twinkle people on straws on to the stage and, soon, they were ready to put on a show for the toys.

10 — "The Dollies Hospital proudly presents a *Twinkle* pantomime," Nancy announced. And everyone *loved* the show!

You can see how to make a Twinkle pantomime, too, inside this book.

Silly Milly

She's always in a muddle

1 — Milly was Christmas shopping in town one day when she saw a poster advertising a competition to make a funny video. "I'll have a go at that!" she exclaimed.

2 — Dad allowed Milly to borrow his camcorder and they set off for the shopping centre. "I'll film all the goings-on in here," said Milly. "I'll call it 'Christmas Capers'."

3 — "Now, *that's* funny," said Milly, bending over a child who was making faces. "Look out!" yelled a man. Too late — he tripped over Milly and his parcels went *everywhere*!

4 — A little later, a black cat ran through the centre. "I must record this!" yelled Milly. She chased after the cat, knocking all the shoppers out of the way.

5 — Then Milly tried to film the whole area. But, as she walked backwards, she fell into the ornamental fountain. "You're soaking us!" cried the people nearby.

6 — Milly and Dad hurried from the centre. "What a laugh!" chuckled Dad's friend, Tom, who worked there as a guard and was watching on the security screen.

7 — Later, Tom called at Milly's house and handed her a video. "Our security cameras recorded everything at the centre this morning," he chuckled. "It's brilliant!"

8 — Milly entered the security video in the competition — and, to her delight, she won *first prize*! "Ho, ho! Sometimes it pays to be silly!" giggled Milly, happily.

Puzzle time

Try to find these words hidden in the toymaker's wordsquare.

TOY MAKER BENCH HAMMER SAW BELL DOLL PRAM

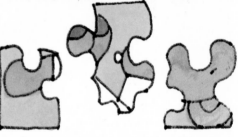

Where do these pieces fit in the jigsaw picture?

There are six differences between these pictures. Try to spot them.

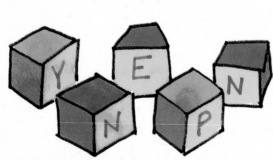

Rearrange these letter blocks to spell the name of a doll.

Answer:- PENNY

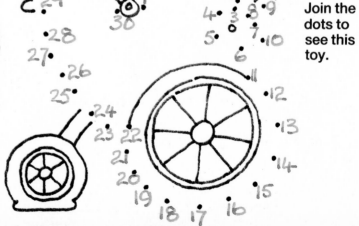

Join the dots to see this toy.

Now here is a super picture to colour with your paints or crayons.
Then find six bells hidden in the picture.

Toyroom tales

EVERY night at midnight, the toys in Tina's bedroom became real.

One night, a *new* toy arrived. Fifi, the fairy doll, fluttered around excitedly.

"Hi! My name's Fifi," she said. "Who are you?"

"I'm Elephant," said the new toy shyly. "And I'm very pleased to meet you."

"This is Spacedog," said Fifi, "and here's Sammy Scarecrow, Soldier, Drummer, Jack in the box and Cara."

"Hello," said all the toys.

Then Spacedog asked, "Would you like to play football?"

Elephant answered, "Yes, please."

But poor Elephant got off to a bad start. Trying to dribble the ball, he tripped himself up and accidentally trod on it instead. *Bang!* The football burst and was squashed completely flat.

2 — Soldier, who was referee, blew his whistle and ordered Spacedog to fetch another ball. Elephant blushed with shame for holding up the game.

3 — Then another mishap. Elephant, trying to make amends, tackled Spacedog who leapt out of the way — leaving Sammy Scarecrow in Elephant's path.

"Oof!" cried Sammy, hopping with pain as Elephant stepped on his foot.

Soldier blew his whistle and called, "Penalty!"

"I'm dreadfully sorry," stammered Elephant. "I didn't mean to do that."

"Penalty!" repeated Soldier firmly.

After that, Elephant's team was one goal down. Drummer turned to Elephant.

"You play right back now and keep out of the way," he grunted.

Elephant nodded miserably, feeling a proper fool.

Spacedog wondered how he could help. Slowly his tail began to spin and his eyes flashed green. This was a sure sign that he was thinking up a good idea. Then he whispered to Elephant who smiled and said, "I'll try."

4 — The score was still one-nil. Elephant kept his eye on the ball and, as soon as it rolled near, he bent down, stretched his trunk out and blew *very, very* hard. The ball shot straight into the net.

"Goal!" yelled Spacedog.

Elephant blew the ball into the net *four* more times and won the match.

All the toys had fun.

"It's much safer when Elephant plays *blow* football," they laughed.

Sally and Scamp

1 — Sally's best friend is her cheeky Shetland pony called Scamp. Just before Christmas, Sally's daddy was decorating the garden trees with fairy lights.

2 — Sally and some of the children from the village were helping. "I wish it would hurry up and snow," said Jenny. "It makes it seem more like Christmas."

3 — Next day, little Tom told Sally his exciting news. "Our nursery class is being taken into town tomorrow to visit Santa," he said. "I'm really excited."

4 — That afternoon, when Sally took Scamp out for a ride, it began to snow. "Hooray!" cried Sally. "Jenny will be pleased. She's got her wish!"

5 — But it snowed so heavily all night and next day, the roads into town were blocked. "Sorry, children, but we can't get in to see Santa," said the teacher.

6 — Kind-hearted Sally couldn't bear to see the little ones so disappointed and, after a word with her daddy, went to see the teacher and told her of her idea.

7 — The teacher was delighted with Sally's plan, and told the children they were in for a treat. If you turn over the page, you, *too,* will see what it is!

It's Sally and reindeer Scamp pulling Santa's sleigh! Now follow the instructions and make a super Christmas scene.

Paste these pages to card and carefully cut out the pictures. Slot the figures and the stands together. To join Scamp and the sleigh together, ask an adult to pierce the black circle on Scamp's harness and the circle on the front of the sleigh.

Loop a piece of string through and tie at the back.

Hi, there!

I ALWAYS have a great time when I go on trips with my Auntie Claire, Uncle David and little cousin, Jamie. So, I was very pleased when they asked Mum and Dad if they could take me out one day during the holidays.

"Where are we going?" I asked curiously.

"Wait and see!" laughed Uncle David.

Over the next few days, I tried desperately to get Mum and Dad to tell me where my aunt and uncle were taking me. But, even though I nagged and nagged, they wouldn't let me in on the secret.

2 — It turned out that we were going to a dinosaur exhibition which had opened a few weeks before at a centre not far from my home town.

Some of my friends had been talking about it, saying that they'd love to go there because it sounded really exciting.

We set off early to avoid the crowds and arrived in time for opening at half-past nine.

The hall was huge and it was just the place to see models of dinosaurs and other creatures on display.

3 — As we walked round the exhibits, I tried to think of a time, long ago, when these amazing animals roamed the Earth.

I'd seen videos about dinosaurs at school but it was different coming face to face with life-size models of them.

"I can't believe how big they were!" I said to Uncle David.

"Yes," Uncle David replied. "Some of them, like Diplodocus, a plant eater, were over twenty-seven metres long. They lived in vast herds which gave them protection from ferocious dinosaurs such as Tyrannosaurus Rex."

Moments later, we arrived at a model of the great T-Rex himself. It was a motorised model which suddenly moved and gave out a mighty roar.

Poor Jamie got such a fright, he burst into tears.

4 — "T-Rex is a bit too realistic for Jamie," said Auntie Claire. "I'll take him to the cafe for a drink of juice, Amy, while you and David see the rest of the exhibition."

Auntie Claire picked up the tearful little boy to give him a cuddle and we arranged to meet up with her later.

Uncle David said that he'd been mad about dinosaurs since he was a little boy and he was able to tell me lots about them.

He pointed out Triceratops which had three great horns on its head. It looked a bit like a rhinoceros, only *much* bigger!

Overhead, hung models of Pteranodons — "great flying lizards" Uncle David called them.

They had enormous wings and it was hard to imagine creatures like these soaring like birds in the sky and diving into the sea to catch fish.

5 — We met Auntie Claire and Jamie again in the cafe and, after lunch, we visited the exhibition shop. There were lots of dinosaur goodies for sale and we bought some souvenirs.

Going home in the car, I thought how envious my chums would be when I told them where I'd spent the day.

Back at my house, Jamie played with the toys Auntie Claire and Uncle David had bought him.

"I think these dinosaurs are a better size for him," laughed Auntie Claire.

6 — "I had a *brilliant* time!" I told Mum and Dad later. "But I'm glad dinosaurs don't live on Earth today."

"Me too!" laughed Dad. "They'd make an awful mess trampling my lawn with their big feet."

After supper, I went upstairs to my bedroom to pin up a super dino poster I'd bought.

I bought a baseball cap with a Stegosaurus on it, too. Pretty smart, don't you think?

See you soon,

Amy.

Happy Snaps

YOU can play this super fun game with your friend. Paste these two pages to card, then cut out all the pictures. There are 16 pairs of matching animal cards.

Mix the cards up, then place them face down on a table. Decide which player goes first.

The first player turns over two cards. If they are a matching pair, the player keeps them, and tries again, continuing until two cards are turned over that aren't a pair. When that happens, the next player takes a turn. The secret of the game is to remember where all the matching cards are.

Once all the matching cards have been collected, count them up. The winner is the player with most pairs.

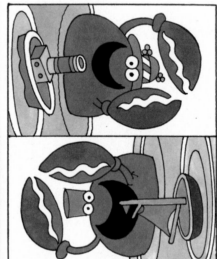

Beauty

MY name is Beauty and I live on a farm with several other horses and ponies. Mr Peters, the owner, bought me for his daughter, Gemma, a kind, gentle girl.

2 — When Gemma grew too big to ride me, she taught me how to pull a pony trap. "Even though we can't go for *proper* rides, Beauty," she told me, "you'll *always* be my favourite."

3 — One bright January day, Gemma tried to persuade Pauline, her sister, to use me and the pony trap for her wedding in the spring. "No way!" cried Pauline. "I want a big fancy car!"

4 — Pauline ordered a white wedding car and, a few months later, Gemma talked eagerly about the big day. "I can't wait for Saturday!" she told me. "But I hope this rain stays away."

5 — It rained non-stop for the next two days. I spent most of my time in a shelter with the other ponies, only coming out now and then for exercise. "I hope it's not like this on Saturday," I thought miserably.

6 — Luckily, Saturday morning was bright and clear. To my surprise, Gemma's dad arrived. "You've an important job to do this morning, Beauty," he said.

7 — Gemma was waiting in the yard. She brushed me until my coat gleamed while Mr Peters cleaned the pony trap. "What's going on?" I wondered. "They should be getting ready for Pauline's wedding."

8 — Gemma explained that the heavy rain had caused a landslip blocking the farm road to all traffic. "We need *you* to take us in the trap!" she said excitedly.

9 — I waited patiently while Gemma and her dad hurried to change into their wedding outfits. When it was time to leave, Mr Peters carried the girls over the puddles to the trap.

10 — Mr and Mrs Peters rode Samuel and Stardust as we made our way across the muddy fields to the village. "Look at those cows watching us," giggled Pauline.

11 — There was great excitement when we arrived. And later, Pauline was delighted to see that some of the villagers had decorated the trap with flowers. "You're better than any old car, Beauty," whispered Gemma. "I *am* proud of you."

Puzzle time

Jilly and her chums are having super fun with their pets. Colour the picture with your paints or crayons. Then try to find these words hidden in the wordsquare.

DONKEY MOUSE PARROT CAT LAMB PONY DOG DUCK GOAT

★ STEP EARPAD ★

Rearrange the letters on the banner to see what they are planning.

D	M	O	C	L	T
T	O	R	R	A	P
Y	U	N	O	M	T
N	S	G	K	B	O
O	E	N	O	E	N
P	K	C	U	D	Y

There are six pet mice in the picture. Can you find two exactly alike?

Now see if you can find the animals in the picture which match these silhouettes.

There's a surprise in store for Nancy. But first she has to do her chores. You can help her by playing this game. First trace or cut out the counters. Then throw a dice to see who starts. First to the finish is the winner.

22

21 Mitzi's dog runs off with doll's bandage. Go back 3 places to catch it.

23 Borrow a pedal car to deliver a toy. Go on 4 places.

20

24

19

25

18

26 Colin has arranged a surprise party for Nancy. Go to finish to join her.

17

27

16

15

28

14 Nancy's hat blows off. Miss a turn while you fetch it.

29

30

Finish

Fairy Fay

1 — Fairy Fay and her friends loved Fairy Baker's wonderful cake shop. "It's the royal birthday party soon," the older fairy told them. "I must bake the Fairy Queen's cake."

2 — "The Fairy Queen's birthday party! How exciting!" cried the fairies. "I wish *I* could go to that," sighed Fay, longingly.

3 — A few days later, however, Fay was surprised to see Fairy Baker closing the shop early. "I feel terrible," she told Fay, sadly. "I'm too ill to bake the queen's cake."

4 — Fay tucked up Fairy Baker in bed and brought her a special cold medicine made from honey, rosehips and blackcurrants.

5 — Then, following Fairy Baker's recipe, she set to work mixing the ingredients for a rich fruit cake. "It smells delicious," thought Fay, happily.

6 — When the cake had cooled from the oven, Fay's friends arrived to help mix the icing sugar. Fay carefully piped pretty pink decorations on to the cake.

7 — The queen was delighted with her cake. She invited Fay and her chums to the party where the proud little fairy was presented with a special medal.

patch

1 — One day, Paula and her kitten, Patch, were watching television. "Look, Patch," said Paula, "the lady is going to show us how to brighten up plain dishes by sticking pictures on to them."

2 — When the programme finished, Paula decided she would try one too! "Mummy's given me an old plate," she told Patch. "So here goes!"

3 — But Paula's first attempt was a disaster! "All my pictures have fallen off!" she cried. "It hasn't worked!" "Never mind," replied Mummy. "Let's start again. I'll help you."

4 — And with Mummy's assistance, Paula managed to decorate a plate, beautifully! "There, doesn't that look pretty?" said Mummy.

5 — A little later, Paula was back at the kitchen table, but she wouldn't let Patch see what she was doing. "You can purr as much as you like," she laughed. "It's to be a surprise!"

6 — On Christmas morning, Patch found out what the surprise was. His very own feeding bowl which Paula had decorated! He *was* pleased! "Happy Christmas to the best kitten in the world!" said Paula.

Old King Cold

2 — Princess Sparkle was happy to see the river flow, but Queen Chilla was troubled.

"It's my fault," she muttered. "I didn't invite the Snow Queen to our ball. Now she's put a spell on us."

DRIP, *drip, drip.* Old King Cold rushed to his balcony to see what was making the noise. He couldn't believe his eyes! All around him, icicles were slowly thawing from his palace made of ice.

"My kingdom is *melting*!" roared the king.

At once, Queen Chilla and Princess Sparkle ran to the drawbridge where the king was crying, "I am ruined! How can I be King of the Ice Kingdom if there's no ice?"

3 — Old King Cold dashed off to apologise to the Snow Queen. When he reached her palace, though, he was told that she had gone off in a terrible temper.

"What can I do now?" sighed the king.

He returned to his melting Ice Kingdom and called some messengers.

"Spread the news that whoever can freeze the kingdom may marry my daughter," he declared.

"What?" gasped Princess Sparkle.

4 — "I want to fall in love before I marry," she sighed.

As the kingdom continued to melt, though, she had no choice.

Young men travelled from far and wide to win the heart and hand of the pretty Ice Princess — but they could not stop the Ice Kingdom from its slow thaw.

Then, one day, as Princess Sparkle ran her fingers through a rippling stream, a stranger approached. The princess thought he was *very* handsome.

"I wish to accept the king's challenge," he said.

Before the king, the stranger spread his icy fingers across the palace and blew his cool misty breath across the kingdom.

5 — At once, as if by magic, the thawing palace and kingdom froze over.

"You've done it!" cried Princess Sparkle.

Then the stranger snapped his fingers and small snow imps appeared, sprinkling flakes of snow.

"You are wonderful!" gasped the princess who, by now, had fallen madly in love.

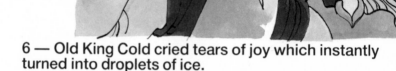

6 — Old King Cold cried tears of joy which instantly turned into droplets of ice.

Princess Sparkle kissed the stranger on the cheek and said, "I shall be *delighted* to marry you!"

Then she added, "But I don't know your name."

"My name is Jack Frost and I am from the Frozen North," explained the young man. "The Snow Queen is my aunt and she told me of her spiteful spell. I wanted to make amends — and marry you, of course," he added.

And *everyone* was happy to see the Ice Princess marry Jack Frost.

Picnic Puzzles

Lead teddy through the maze to reach the picnic spot.

Can you find six differences between those two pictures?

HONEY

HO EY

Count the apples and then find two which are exactly the same.

Find six things beginning with the letter "C" in this picture then finish colouring it.

Chocs

BUNS

How to make a
Twinkle Pantomime

Your Twinkle chums are dressed up to put on a Cinderella pantomime.

Cut out the thick black lines around the figures and tape a drinking straw to the back of each.

Next, find a large grocery box to turn into a theatre.

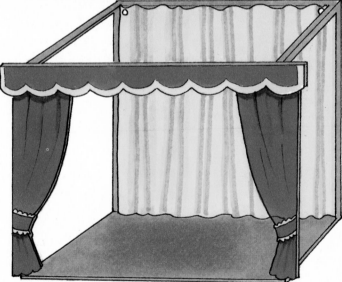

Take out the sides of the box, leaving only a "floor" and frame. Pin a piece of material to the frame at the back of the "stage". Next, make a pelmet and curtains from thin card *wider* than the front of your theatre and stick it on.

The straws may be taped to whichever side of the figure suits to let you slip them on to the stage from either side, through the back or even from the top.

Now, do you know who everyone is? Doesn't Scamp look proud pulling Cinderella's golden coach? Poor Nancy is working hard as Cinders, while Paula, her wicked stepmother, orders her to scrub the floor. Isn't little Benny sweet, carrying the glass slipper on a cushion?

Patch looks petrified as Silly Milly puts a spell on him — her spell's *bound* to go wrong! Will he turn into a pumpkin for the Fairy Godmother?

Now, at the ball, Cinderella dances with Prince Charming (Colin) while her ugly sisters (Twinkle and Amy) look on.

Have fun with your Twinkle pantomime!

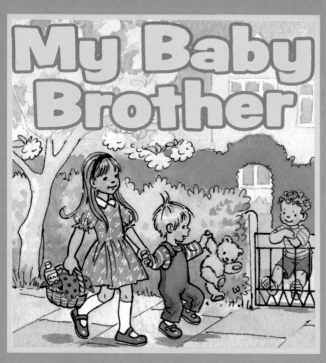

My Baby Brother

MY brother Ben's a friendly chap,
   He has so many pals.
Now some of them are "people" friends,
   And some are animals . . .

There's Purr the puss, who lives next door.
   When Benny goes to call
He tells her secret pussy tales,
   As they sit on the wall.

Matthew the milkman is a mate
   Who Benny loves to see.
"Be sure to drink your pinta up,
   Then you'll be strong as me!"

Pip Postman is another pal,
   He whistles all the way.
Ben is excited when he shouts,
   "A card for you, today!"

Across the street lives Ben's pal, Pete,
    As cheeky as can be.
They always have a noisy fight
    When Pete comes round to tea.

Just down the lane is donkey Jane,
    A carrot makes her day.
When she sees Benny bringing one,
    She gives a happy bray.

Ben likes to visit Mrs Blair,
    Who runs the village shop.
He spends his pocket money there,
    Then hurries home, hop-hop.

But can you guess who's Ben's *best* friend
    The one he takes to bed,
And carries round with him all day?
    Of course, it's dear old Ted!

Jenny and her brother, Tom, are going Christmas shopping. You can join in the fun by playing this game. Trace or cut out the counters on the right, then throw a dice to see who starts. First to reach the Christmas party at the finish wins.

PAY HERE

MEGA

16

17

Groan! Stuck in long queue with Mum. Go back 2 places.

18

19

20

21

22

23
Get your present from Santa, but then have to wait for little brother! Miss a turn.

24
Help Auntie with her shopping. Go on 3 places.

TAXIS

HIRE

24

25

26
Oops! You've picked up the wrong shopping bag. Go back 5 places to swap it.

27

28

29

finish

The jungle pool

THE animals were having fun sploshing about and cooling off in the jungle pool one very hot day. The monkeys were floating in old tyres while little Leo Lion swung on a rope, letting go every now and then to drop into the pool.

Rory Rhino and Eddie Elephant were playing ball when, suddenly, as Rory missed the ball, a green head popped out of the water and caught it in *very* sharp teeth!

Hiss! The ball burst and Kris Crocodile called, "Got you!" and he grinned a cheeky grin, showing off his shiny sharp teeth.

2 — Another day, when the monkeys were playing hide and seek, Kris quickly stuck his head out from under a bush and snapped at them — *snap, snap*!

"Eek!" they shrieked, and their game was ruined.

3 — Later, in the pool, Kris caught the tip of Tony Tiger's tail.

"That was *not* funny!" roared Rory as Kris crept away on the far bank of the pool. "You're a real spoilsport!"

"The trouble is we can't see him coming underwater," said Eddie.

"Let's build our very own swimming pool and only let in who we want," suggested Harriet Hippo.

Good idea," laughed Jilly Giraffe, "but it would be a lot of work."

4 — "We're strong. We'll *build* a pool!" cried Rory and Eddie.

"Hooray!" cheered the animals, and they all agreed to help.

Harriet chose a site, far away from the river — and Kris, then she drew up plans for her specially-designed pool. It looked super with twirly slides and wave machines.

The jungle animals worked really hard and, soon, a big wall was built around the site and work began on the pool. Harriet *was* pleased at how it was coming on.

5 — When, at last, the pool was ready, the animals decided that Harriet Hippo should perform the opening ceremony.

Everyone wore their best swimsuits and crowded round the pool as Harriet took a long run towards a springboard.

Boing! She somersaulted into the pool!

6 — Then, a horrible howl was heard — "*Yeowl*!"

Harriet leapt out of the pool in alarm and everyone gasped, then laughed, when they saw Kris Crocodile stagger out, looking dazed.

"Oh!" he groaned. "My head."

The nasty crocodile had been spying on the animals all along and had sneaked into the grounds in a cement mixer. During the night, he'd crept into the pool. He hadn't reckoned on Harriet Hippo diving in and flattening him, though.

The animals cheered as Rory Rhino and Eddie Elephant marched Kris away and locked him out. After that, Kris Crocodile was never seen again and the animals had brilliant fun in their jungle pool!

Nursery rhymes

I LOVE the old, old nursery rhymes
  That Granny reads to me.
There's "Jack and Jill went up the hill,"
  My favourite, you see.

Remember Tom, the piper's son?
  He stole a pig, you know,
And Mary, with her little lamb,
  Whose fleece was white as snow.

I love the tale of wee Boy Blue
  Who fell so fast asleep,
He quite forgot to keep an eye
  On all the cows and sheep.

"Hickory, Dickory, Dock" reads Gran,
  She shows the pic to me —
The little mouse runs up the clock,
  As quickly as can be.

Poor Pussy fell into the well.
  But it's all right, you see,
For now I see him sitting here,
  As happy as can be!

Betty Buttercup

1 — Betty Buttercup lives in Garden City where everyone is named after flowers or plants. She was going to a Fancy Dress party with Ragged Robin.

2 — "I wish I could go to the party as well," sighed their friend, Snapdragon. "But there aren't any costumes suitable for dragons to wear!"

3 — As the party-goers set off, a gust of wind blew away Robin's cowboy hat.

4 — When the little boy finally caught up with his hat, his costume was in tatters! "I can't go like this!" he wailed. "I must go and change."

5 — With Robin wearing his new costume, the pair set off again. "I know a short-cut through here," he said. "Look at these jaggy bushes!" exclaimed Betty.

6 — As they argued, Witch Hazel appeared. "What you need is a knight in shining armour," she said, and with a few waves of her wand that's what Robin became!

7 — In his armour, Robin was able to hack his way through the woods, allowing him and Betty to arrive at the party in time. And Snapdragon was able to go to the party as his partner. Everyone cheered as they won first prize.

Honey

She's sweet but full of fun!

1 — Honey's mummy was making her a new dress. "Try this on," she told Honey. The little bear groaned. She couldn't *wait* to get to the funfair.

2 — When she reached the fair at last, Honey looked around for her friends. "I hope I can find them," she sighed. "It won't be much fun on my own."

3 — Clever Honey had an idea. She hopped into an aeroplane ride which went high in the sky. "I'll spot them from up here," she thought. "Yes! There they are!"

4 — Honey's chums were just going on to the dodgem cars. "Wait for me!" called Honey, and she jumped into another car. The friends had great fun whizzing round.

5 — Afterwards, Honey had a go at the hoopla stall. She was *very* good at throwing the hoops over the objects. Her chums *were* impressed! "Well done!" they cried.

6 — Back home, Honey peeped round the door and called, "Mum, meet Betsy!" "Oh, you should have warned me you were bringing her home for tea," said Mum.

7 — Honey grinned. "She doesn't need tea, Mum," she laughed. "She's a toy that I won at the fair! Now *she* can model my dress while I go out to play!"

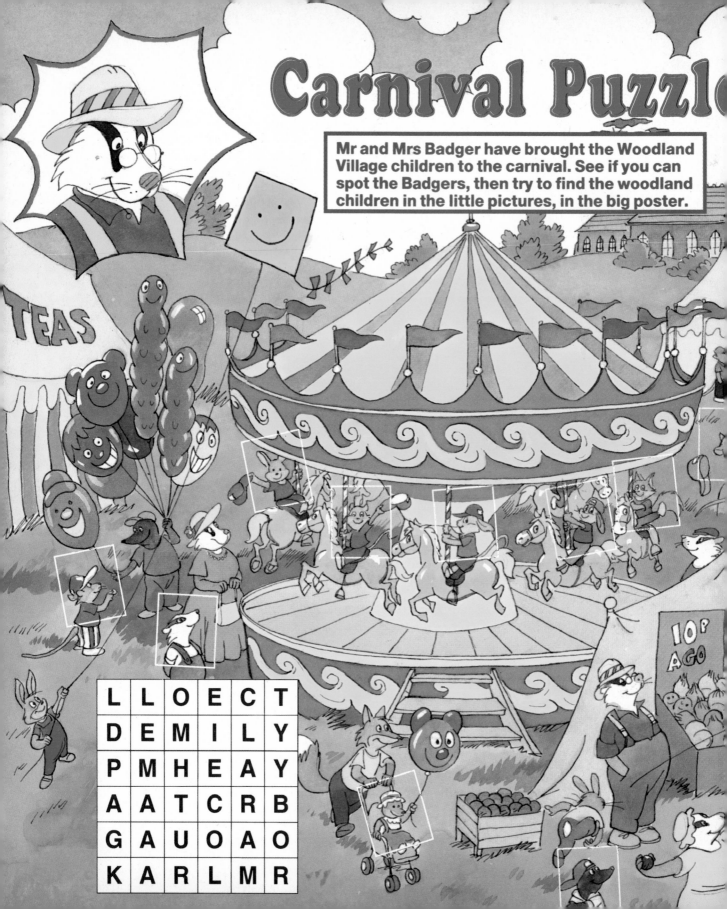

I know somewhere that *is* warm, though.

Farmer Brown's greenhouse is just perfect!

Carrie

What do you call a deer who can see well?

A good eye-deer!

What do angry mice send each other at Christmas?

Cross-mouse cards!

I know who'll clear it for me. Hello, Ferdy?

Ho, ho! Ferdy is a fox and the name for his tail is a brush! Thanks for your help.

Puzzle time

Suzy and her friends are going carol singing. How many of these words can you find hidden on her songsheet?

CAROL SONG CANDLE BELL LAMP SNOW ROBIN

R	L	S	R	A	B
C	A	R	O	L	E
A	M	C	B	N	W
L	P	E	I	O	G
E	L	D	N	A	C
L	E	S	O	B	E

Join the dots to see what Suzy is going to carry.

Only two of these handbells are exactly alike. Can you spot them?

Everybody is dressed and ready to go now. Try to find six differences between these two pictures of them waving goodbye.

Rearrange the letters on the songsheet to see what song the children are singing.

While the children are singing, you can join in the fun by colouring the picture with your paints or crayons.

Now try to find where the small pictures above fit in the big picture. Then look for six robins hidden in the picture.

BODKIN BEAR'S fun park was very exciting. The animals from Willow Wood *loved* it! It had a big wheel and a boating lake, dodgem cars and roundabouts and, the biggest thrill of all, a huge water chute. How the animals loved whizzing down its slope and splashing into the water!

The fun park also had a witch who could do all sorts of magic. She was really an owl called Witchy Woo who wore a red robe and a pointed hat. Witchy Woo had a book of magic spells but, sadly, they often went wrong.

Bodkin Bear was getting worried. It hadn't rained for a long time and the water for the pond and water chute was getting low.

2 — Bodkin went to see Witchy Woo.
"Can you do some magic to make it rain?" he asked. "Things are getting desperate."

"Of course," hooted Witchy, and she twittered some rain-making spells from her book.

Then they waited.

3 — But, instead of rain, there came a terrible wind. *Whoo*! It blew and blew until it blew away all the water that was left in the boating pond.

"Help!" squeaked Timmy Mouse from his boat. "I'm grounded!"

But no one heard him.

"I'm terribly sorry," muttered Witchy to Bodkin. "I think it must have been the wrong spell I put on the weather. I'll try again."

4 — She opened her book and hooted some more magic words. The wind died down but, then, there was an awful roar of thunder and a flash of lightning — but still no rain. The thunder grew louder and the lightning flashed faster and, suddenly, the fun park amusements stopped altogether. The animals *were* annoyed because the forks of lightning stopped the dodgem cars.

"Aww!" shouted Rosie Rabbit and her brother from her dodgem car that shuddered to a halt. "When can we get going again?"

5 — "I thought you could perform *magic*!" shouted Bodkin Bear angrily to Witchy Woo.

"Sorry," sniffed Witchy Woo nervously. "I'll try just *once* more."

And she flicked the pages of her spell book. She hooted more magic words in desperation, and this time, she waved her wand, too. Bodkin waited anxiously.

6 — But things got even *worse*!

"Oh, no!" screamed Bodkin Bear. "Now you've made it *snow*, you silly owl. *Everything's* covered! And look at my water chute! It's like a snowy *mountainside*!"

Witchy suddenly had a brilliant idea. She wrote on the chute, "Roll up and try the great toboggan slide!"

Bodkin's water chute had now become an exciting toboggan and ski slope. The animals *loved* its breathtaking ride, once they had put on warm clothes, of course!

Witchy sighed with relief. Her magic had turned out okay, after all.

"Well done, Witchy," laughed Bodkin Bear. "You've saved the fun park from being a washout," he added with a chuckle.

Twinkle

is on sale
Every Wednesday

Packed with stories, puzzles, competitions, things to do.

ORDER YOUR COPY NOW

Cut out this coupon and hand it to your newsagent.
Please keep a copy of "Twinkle" for me every week.

NAME _____

ADDRESS _____

_____

Parents/Guardian's Signature ....

Play the Winter Sports Game with Silly Milly

Start

1

2 Milly wins acrobatic skiing contest — by accident! Go on 4 places.

3

4

5 Milly packs wrong skating boots. Go back 2 places.

6

7

8

9 Huskies run off with Milly's dog sleigh. Miss a turn while she chases it.

10

11 Silly Milly is silly enough to go in ice hockey goal. Throw dice to see how many goals you score against her. Then go forward that number.

12

13

14

15